THE STORY OF

THE THREE KINGS

THE STORY OF THE THREE KINGS:

Melchior, Balthasar and Jaspar, which originally was written

by JOHN OF HILDESHEIM in the fourteenth century

and is now retold by Margaret B. Freeman

New York · The Metropolitan Museum of Art

Published by The Metropolitan Museum of Art, 1955
Reprinted 1978, 1979

Library of Congress catalogue card number 55-12148
Standard Book Number 0-87099-180-9

A few years ago while preparing an exhibition for The Cloisters entitled "Wise Men from the East" I became acquainted for the first time with John of Hildesheim's Story of the Three Kings. Those who saw the exhibition were as enchanted with the tale as I, and many of them have urged me to "put it in a book." And so here it is.

The text of the story of the three Kings was originally written in Latin sometime between 1364 and 1375. As early as 1389 it was translated into German and about 1400 it appeared in English. Somewhat later it was translated into French, Flemish and Dutch. At present it exists in many manuscript versions and in many printed editions, the first having been published in Cologne in 1477.

Though the book found great favor in the Middle Ages, it was considered of no value at all by a later, more critical era that could not accept the story as credible history nor yet enjoy it as a legend full of marvels and mystery. And so for centuries it lay neglected and forgotten. Then, in 1818, Goethe discovered a Latin manuscript of The Story of the Three Kings and was charmed by it. This manuscript was published in a modern German version in 1822 by Gustaf Schwab. In 1886 Carl Horstmann, regretting that "this book, extremely popular in its day...has been forgotten since," published for The Early English Text Society two early fifteenth-century manuscripts of the story which had been translated into English as The Three Kings of Cologne. These manuscripts are the basis for the present text.

In rewriting the story I have added certain details from the Latin and German texts and I have omitted from the original much that seemed extraneous and dull. I have reorganized and suppressed but I have kept the essentials of the story intact and have tried also to keep the flavor of the English that Chaucer knew.

The illustrations and the general format are from Leben der heiligen drei Königen in The Pierpont Morgan Library, one of the rare copies of the edition of John of Hildesheim's story published by Heinrich Knoblochtzer in Strassburg about 1484. Of the fifty-eight woodcuts (four repeats) in the original publication all have been included here that seemed pertinent to this revised version of the tale.

And now, here is the story of the three Kings: for B. A. B., J. D. and E. N. L., for the members of The Cloisters staff, and for all those who, having read many times of what the Magi did at the birth of Christ, would peradventure like to know what these three Kings did afterward.

Margaret B. Freeman

Here begins

THE STORY OF
THE THREE KINGS

Prologue: This is the story of the life and deeds of the three
Kings who came to worship Our Lord at his birth

F the three worshipful Kings all the world is full
of praise from the rising of the sun to its down=
going, and what these three Kings did at the
birth of Our Lord Jesus Christ is written oft in
many books and places but what they did after
is peradventure to many men unknown. But there be many
books written in Hebrew and Chaldean of the life and deeds
of these Kings, the which books were brought out of India
and the East by the princes of Vaus who were of the blood
of Melchior, King of Nubia, the same who offered gold to
Our Lord Jesus as ye shall hear after. These books of the
life and deeds of the three Kings were brought to the city of

Acre, along with the golden diadem of King Melchior and many other wonderful ornaments, in the year of Our Lord one thousand and two hundred. And these books written in Hebrew and Chaldean were afterwards translated into French. And so of these books and divers other books and of sermons and homilies and also of seeing and hearing and speaking to other men, there has been written and put together one book.

Here the princes of Vaus arrive at the city of Acre

Chapter 1: Balaam prophesies concerning the star and the birth of Christ

HIS matter of the three blessed Kings took its beginning in the prophecy of Balaam, the Priest of Madian, who prophesied and said: "A star shall spring out of Jacob and a man shall rise upon Israel and shall be lord of all folk."

Wherefore, in that time that Balaam so gloriously prophesied of the incarnation of Our Lord Jesus and of the star, then all the great lords and all the other people of India desired greatly to see that star.

Now there was in that land a hill called Vaus, the which was also called the Hill of Victory. And inasmuch as this hill passed in height all the hills in the country of India, divers keepers were ordained to watch there night and day so that men in the lands about might not with a strong hand enter into the kingdom. Wherefore the people of India promised great gifts to the keepers of the Hill of Vaus if it were that by day or night, far or near, they should see any light or any star in the firmament other than was seen beforetime. And they also ordained twelve of the wisest men and greatest clerks of astronomy that were in all the country about to watch on the hill, some at one time and some another. And the more that this star was looked after, the more the fame of this star increased and was spoken of throughout the land of India and Chaldea, and all the people desired to see it. For in those days the Chaldeans gave much time to astronomy and had great delight therein, insomuch that every maid and every child in men's houses did know the course of the stars.

This is the Hill of Vaus in the land of India

Chapter 2: Our Lord is born in Bethlehem for the salvation of mankind

OW, as Saint Luke telleth when the time was come that the Father of Heaven would have mercy on all mankind and send down his Son to take flesh and blood of Our Lady Saint Mary and to be born man of her for the salvation of all the world, Octavius, Emperor of Rome, sent out a commandment to tax all men. So every man went into his own country. Then went Joseph out of Galilee that is a city in Nazareth into the city of King David, the which city was called Bethlehem, for Joseph was of the household and the lineage of King David. And he went into that country with Our Lady Saint Mary that was his wife and also great with child.

5

And ye shall understand that Bethlehem was never of any great reputation; it was but a castle but it was called a city because King David was born there. And in that town was at that time the house in which King David was born. And in the same place Christ, God's Son, was born of Our Lady Saint Mary the Holy Virgin. But at the time of the nativity of Our Lord that house was all destroyed—insomuch that there was nothing left but broken walls on every side and a little cave under the earth and a little unthrifty house before the cave. And here men sold bread on the same ground. And timber and other things that were brought to market and were not sold were put into this little house until the next market; and asses and horses and other beasts were tied about this un= thrifty house.

Now when Joseph and Our Lady Saint Mary riding on an ass came late in eventide toward the city of Bethlehem—because they came so late and all places were occupied with pilgrims and other men, and also because they came in poor array, they went about the city and no man would rescue them. And Our Lady Mary, a young woman sitting on an ass, was full weary of the way and nigh at the time of bearing her child. Then Joseph led Our Lady into this forlorn place that no man took care of, down into the little dark house. And in that house in the cave of old time was left a manger and to that manger was tied an ox of a poor man that no one would har= bor, and beside that ox Joseph tied his ass. And in that little house Our Lord Jesus was that same night born of Our Lady the Blessed Virgin without any pain or sorrow of her body for the salvation of all mankind.

And Our Lady wrapped her blessed Son in cloths and laid him in the hay in the manger before the ass and the ox, for there was no other place.

6

Chapter 3: The shepherds hear the message from the angel
of heaven

ND shepherds were nearby in the same coun=
try keeping their sheep in the night. And an
angel of heaven came and stood by them with
a great light, whereof they were greatly adread.
But the angel said to them: "Be not afraid for
I tell you a great joy that shall be to all people; for this day is
born to us Our Lord Jesus Christ in the City of David. And
this shall be to you a token: ye shall find a young Child wrap=
ped in cloths and put in a manger." And suddenly there came
a great multitude of angels of heaven praising God and say=
ing: "Joy be to God on high and peace on earth to men of
good will."

7

Now betwixt Bethlehem and that place where the angel appear=
ed unto the shepherds was but half a mile and a little way
more. And ye shall understand that in that same place King
David, when he was a little child, fed sheep and kept them from
the lion.

And furthermore ye shall understand that the land about
Bethlehem and all the land of the East is wonderfully planned
and set with mountains for the most part. By Bethlehem are
many fat pastures, hotter than in other places, insomuch that
at Christmas time barley beginneth to wax ripe; and that time
we call here Christmas is called there the time of herbs. And as
there was no great cold thereabout, the shepherds all that win=
ter, night and day, now in one place now in another, dwelled
there with their sheep and so they do until this day. And as
the worshipful clerk Saint Bede said in his writing, it was full
convenient that the shepherds were awake that night about
their sheep, for He was born that night that said: "I am the
Good Shepherd. A good shepherd giveth his life for his sheep."

Chapter 4: The astronomers on the Hill of Vaus see the star that was prophesied by Balaam

HEN Christ was born of Our Lady Saint Mary
for the salvation of all mankind, as it was afore=
said, then this star that was prophesied by
Balaam and a long time looked for by the twelve
astronomers on the Hill of Vaus—on that same
night and the same hour that Our Lord was born, that same
star began to arise in the manner of a sun brightly shining.
And it ascended above the hill and all that day it stirred not.
And when the sun was most hot and most high there was no
difference in shining betwixt the star and the sun. And the
star had in it the form and likeness of a young child and above

him a sign of the cross; and a voice was heard in the star
saying: "Unto us is born this day the King and Lord that folk
have long sought. Go then and seek him and do him worship."
Then all the people, both men and women of the country about,
when they saw this wonderful and marvellous star and also
heard the voice out of the star, they were greatly aghast and
had great wonder thereof. And the people wist well that it was
the same star that was prophesied by Balaam.

And the twelve wise clerks of astronomy, aforesaid, stood
on that high Hill of Vaus in silence and in prayer. And when
there appeared to them in the middle of the night this bright
shining star with the image of a little child bearing with him
the sign of the cross, they were right joyful that this star was
shown in their time and also that they were worthy to see that
sight. And anon they came down from this high hill and told
to the wisemen of that land all that they had seen and heard.

9

Chapter 5: The three Kings, each in his own land, see the star at the same hour

OW there were three worshipful Kings that in that time reigned in India. And when they were informed by the astronomers of this star, they were right glad. And anon, though each one of them was far from the other, each one of them saw the star at one hour and at the same time. And though no one of them knew of the other's purpose, all three ordained and purposed to go seek and worship the Lord and King as the voice of the star had commanded, spoken and preached. Now pagans that had no knowledge of holy writ nor of the birth of Christ called these three Kings Magi; and the Jews, that knew the scriptures and the birth of Christ, because of envy and falseness called them Magi also. And so it was

10

brought into use and continued to this day. But without doubt they were glorious and worshipful kings; and of all the lands and kingdoms in the East they were the most mighty, as Christian men that dwell there bear witness.

Chapter 6: These are the three Indies where the three Kings reigned at the time that Christ was born

NOW ye shall understand that there be three Indies of which these three lords were kings. In the first India was the land of Nubia and also the land of Arabia; and in those lands reigned Melchior at the time that Christ was born. Now, a man may lightly sail into this India out of Egypt and Syria by the Red Sea. And pilgrims and merchants that pass from

India by the Red Sea say that all the ground of the Red Sea is so red that the water above seems as though it were red wine, notwithstanding that the water is of the color that other water is. And ye shall understand that all the earth in the land of Arabia is red; and also stones and trees and all other things

Here the men of Jaspar's land are gathering myrrh

that grow in that land for the most part are red. And in that land is found gold wonderfully red, and that gold is the best gold that is in all the world.

In the second India was the kingdom of Godolia and the king=dom which men called Saba; and of these kingdoms Balthasar was king, and this Balthasar offered incense to God. And ye shall understand that in this land many good spices grow—more than in all the other countries of the East; and especially there groweth incense more than in all the other places of the world; it drippeth out of certain trees in the manner of gum.

In the third India was the kingdom called Tharsis; and of that kingdom Jaspar was king, the which Jaspar offered myrrh to God. In his isles myrrh groweth more plentifully than in any other place in the world. It groweth like ears of wheat and it waxeth right thick; when it is ripe it is so soft that it cleaveth on men's clothes as they go by the way. And for harvesting, men take small cords and girdles and draw them about the ears, and the myrrh cleaveth upon these cords and then after= wards the myrrh is wrung out of them.

Wherefore ye shall understand that all this was done with great ordinance and mercy of God that these three Kings, Melchior, Balthasar and Jaspar, should come from such lands and kingdoms in which these three gifts, gold and incense and myrrh, the which should be offered to God, did wax and grow.

Chapter 7: The three Kings, all unknown to one another, pre= pare for the journey, and each King goes forth from his kingdom to follow the star

OW these three Kings did each of them prepare for his journey with great and rich gifts and divers ornaments belonging to a king's array, and also with mules and camels and horses loaded with treasure and with a great multitude of people in the best array that was possible for them. They also took with them all manner of necessaries that belonged to bedding or to chamber or to kitchen and all manner of things that belonged to man's meat or beast's meat—of every= thing a great plenty that should suffice them all the way, both outward and homeward. Though there be fair hostels in many

13

places and towns in the East with all manner of victuals for man and beast, it is the custom in that country for lords that ride with a great multitude to carry all necessaries with them

Here Jaspar goes forth from his kingdom

on mules or camels, for it is more profitable to them and more honest. And for the most part men go and ride all night because of the great heat and burning of the sun by day.
Now these three worshipful Kings passed forth out of their kingdoms and no one of them knew of the other nor knew of the other's purpose because of the long way and far way that was betwixt each one of these kingdoms. Yet the star went before every one of these Kings, shining brightly and giving light to each one and his host all the way.
And as it was written, in the time that Christ was born there

14

was peace in all the world; wherefore in all the cities and towns that these worthy Kings rode by there was no gate shut neither by night nor by day. But because of the shining of the star it seemed to all that the night was the day. Wherefore all men of these cities and towns that these worthy Kings rode by in the night were wonderfully aghast and passingly marvelled thereof. And great speech was in all the country among all the people a long time after.

Now these three Kings rode over divers lands, kingdoms, cities and towns; they rode over hills, waters, valleys, plains, and other divers perilous places without any pain or trouble, for all the way that they went, were it high or low, all seemed to them even and plain and a fair way. They never took harbor by the way, nor rested themselves night or day, nor did they eat or drink until they came into Bethlehem. And all this time seemed but a day.

And thus by the great mercy of God and the guidance of the star, these three worthy Kings came out of their lands and kingdoms into Jerusalem on the twelfth day after Christ was born at the uprising of the sun. And if ye wonder at the great speed of their journey, ye shall understand that the Lord God in the Old Testament led Habakkuk the Prophet by the hair of the head out of Judea into Babylon to Daniel that was in a pit among the lions all in a moment—the which is a hundred days' journey coming and going. And that same Lord God in the New Testament was mighty enough to lead these three Kings out of the East into the land of Judea in thirteen days without any trouble or bother. And ye shall understand that God Almighty might have brought these three Kings and all their hosts out of the East into Judea in a moment as he brought Habakkuk the Prophet to Daniel, yet he wanted to make known his marvellous birth to all the world and to the people whom the three Kings passed on their way.

Chapter 8: The three Kings journey to Jerusalem and meet
outside the city where the three highways come
together

HEN these three blessed Kings, each one going
his own way with his host and his company,
were almost come to Jerusalem save for two
miles, then a great dark cloud hid all the earth
and in that dark cloud they lost the star. Of
this Isaiah had prophesied, saying: "Jerusalem, arise and take
light for thy light is come and the joy of God is upon thee,
for lo, darkness shall cover the earth and a cloud thy people,
but the Lord shall arise upon thee and his glory shall be seen
upon thee, and the Gentiles shall walk in thy light, and kings
in the brightness of thy rising."
When these three Kings were nigh Jerusalem, then Melchior,

16

King of Nubia and of Arabia, with his people came first be=
side Jerusalem, by the hill of Calvary where Christ was put
on the cross.

Now there was beside this hill a highway where three ways
came together. And Melchior abode there in a cloud and in
darkness in accordance with the will of God.

And a little after the time that Melchior had come nigh unto
Jerusalem, then came Balthasar, King of Saba, and his host,
and he stopped under the cloud beside the hill of Olivet in a
little town that is called there Galilee, where the disciples of
Almighty God before his resurrection and after were wont to
come together. And so because of the darkness of the cloud
and also because they knew not their way, they abode still
and went no further at that time.

And then this cloud began to ascend and to wax clear though
the star appeared not. But these two Kings each took his way
toward the city with all his host. And when they came to this
highway beside Mount Calvary where the three ways met to=
gether, then along the third highway came Jaspar, King of
Tharsis, and all his host.

And so these three glorious Kings, each one with his host
and his beasts, met together on this highway beside the hill
of Calvary. And notwithstanding that no one of them ever
before had seen the other nor known of him nor his coming,
yet at their meeting each of them with great gladness and
great reverence kissed each other and made much joy. And
though they were of divers languages, yet each one of them
in accordance with his understanding spoke all one manner
of speech.

And when they thus had met together and each one of them
had told to the others his will and intent, and all their wills
were accordingly one, they were more glad than ever. And
so they rode forth into Jerusalem at the uprising of the sun.

17

Chapter 9: The three Kings arrive at the gates of Jerusalem and go to visit Herod who was king of that land and city

OW when the three Kings learned that Jerusalem was the King's city they were right glad, supposing to have found the King of the Jews born in that city. And ye shall understand that at this time Herod was king of that land and he was present in Jerusalem. Furthermore ye shall understand that Herod the King and all the city of Jerusalem were greatly disturbed at the sudden coming of the three Kings, for their hosts and their company and their beasts were of so great a multitude that the city could not receive them. And so for the most part they abode outside the city in the land all about.

18

And when the three Kings came into the city of Jerusalem they asked the people concerning the Child that was born; whereof speaketh the Evangelist Matthew in his gospel that he wrote: "When Christ was born in Bethlehem in the days of Herod that was then king of that same land, three Kings came out of the East and said, 'Where is he that is born King of the Jews for we have seen his star in the East and we are come to worship him.' When Herod the King heard this, he was disturbed and all Jerusalem with him and he gathered together all the princes of the priests and asked of them where Christ should be born. And they said, 'In Bethlehem of Judea. Thus it is written by the prophets...' Then Herod privately called to him these Kings and learned of them the time of the star that appeared to them and so sent forth into Bethlehem and said: 'Go and inquire diligently of this child and when ye have found him, come again and tell me, that I too may come and worship him.'" Now ye shall understand that Herod was but an alien in the land and was made king by the Emperor and the Romans, and he was therefore adread lest he should lose his kingdom because Christ was born. And when the three Kings were informed by Herod and the doctors of the law of Christ's birth and the place where he was born, they passed out of the city of Jerusalem and went their way. And the star appeared to them again as it did before, and it went before them until they came into Bethlehem, the which is but two little miles from Jerusalem.

19

Chapter 10: The three Kings meet the shepherds on the way to Bethlehem

ND nearby that place, as it was aforesaid, were the shepherds to whom the angel appeared with great light and told them of the birth of Christ. Now these three Kings rode by the same place where the shepherds were and spoke with them. And when the shepherds saw the star they ran together, saying that in such a light and in such a clearness the angel had appeared unto them. Furthermore, all that the angel had spoken to them and all that they had heard and seen and all things that were done—they told everything to the three Kings. Whereof the Kings were right glad and of good cheer and were greatly comforted. Some books in the East say that the voice that was heard out of the star was

20

the voice of the same angel that showed the birth of Christ both to the shepherds and to the three Kings. And while the three Kings spoke with these shepherds, the star more and more began to shine brighter and brighter. And when these three glorious Kings had spoken to these shepherds and had given them great gifts, they rode forth on their way.

Chapter 11: The three Kings arrive at the little house in Beth=
lehem where Christ was born

OW when these three blessed Kings knew that they were come to that place of Bethlehem, then they alighted from their horses and changed all their clothing and clothed themselves in new and worshipful clothing, as kings should be arrayed. And when they were so arrayed they again rode

forth. And always the star went before them, and the nearer the Kings came to the place where Christ was, the more the star shone brighter and brighter.

And so they came to Bethlehem in the sixth hour of the day. And these three Kings rode down the street until they came to the little house where Christ was. At this place the star stood still on the ground before this little house and soon after rose up with such a great light that all the little house was full of light, and then anon the star ascended higher and abode above the place where Christ and Our Lady were.

And when the three Kings came to the entrance of the little house they alighted from their horses and went in and found Our Lady and her Child. Ye shall understand that Our Lord Jesus was at that time a little child of thirteen days and he was somewhat fat and lay wrapped in poor cloths in hay in a manger. And Our Lady Saint Mary his mother, as it is written in divers books, was in person fleshy and somewhat brown; and in the presence of these three Kings she was covered with a white mantle which she held closed before her with her left hand; and her head was covered altogether save her face with a linen cloth. And she sat beside the manger and with her right hand she lifted up the Christ Child's head.

Chapter 12: The three Kings offer their gifts of gold and frank= incense and myrrh to the Christ Child

NOW when these three Kings were come into this little house and found Our Lady and her Child and the so=great light of the star, they fell down and worshiped him and offered to him gifts—gold, incense and myrrh.

And ye shall understand that these Kings had worshipfully brought out of their lands many rich gifts and many rich

22

ornaments; that is to say, all the ornaments that Alexander of Macedonia left in India and Chaldea and Persia and all the ornaments that the Queen of Saba offered in Solomon's temple—the which, at the time of the destruction of Jerusalem, were taken into her country by the people of Persia and Chaldea—and many other treasures, both in gold and silver, and precious jewels and stones. All these things were brought with them to offer to God. But when these three Kings found Our Lady and Our Lord Jesus in poor array and the star giving so great a light in all the place, it seemed to them as though they stood in a furnace of fire. Then they were so in awe that of all the rich jewels and stones and ornaments that they brought with them, when their treasures were opened they took out nothing but that thing that they happened to touch first with their hands.

Melchior, King of Nubia and Arabia, who was smallest of stature, took of his treasury a round apple of gold, the which was as much as a man might easily enclose in his hands, and thirty gilt pennies, and these he offered to God. Balthasar, King of Saba, who was medium of stature, took out of his treasury incense, as it came first to his hand, and that he offered to God. Jaspar, King of Tharsis and of the isles, who was tallest of person and a black Ethiope without any doubt, took out of his treasury myrrh, and that he offered to God with tears.

And these three worshipful Kings were so in awe and so devout and fervent in their oblation that of all the words that Our Lady said at that time, they remembered only that to every King as he offered his gift, she bowed her head meekly and said "Deo gracias"; that is to say, "I thank God," or "Thanks be to God."

But ye shall understand that the apple of gold that Melchior the King offered with the thirty gold pennies at one time belonged to Alexander the Great, who did make it of small pieces of gold, the which he had gathered as tribute from all the world. And this apple had been left in India when he came with many rich ornaments.

Of these three gifts that were offered to God divers books and scriptures speak diversely. But it is believed that by gold was shown the power of a king, for gold pertaineth to tribute; by incense was shown divine majesty, for incense pertaineth to sacrifice; by myrrh was shown man's mortality, for myrrh pertaineth to burial.

Though certain books say that gold was offered to help Our Lady and her Son because of poverty, be it understood that though God Almighty lowered himself to become man and was born of his blessed mother Mary, yet he had no need of these gifts of these three worshipful Kings, for he had made

24

all the world out of nothing and all that is in heaven and in earth by his power and by his will.

And what was done afterwards with these gifts which the three Kings offered to God, ye shall hear at a later time.

Chapter 13: The three Kings are warned by an angel to return home to their kingdoms by another way

OW when these three Kings had taken leave of Our Lady, they and all their men and horses and other beasts began to eat and drink and sleep and take their rest; and they desported all that day afterwards in Bethlehem, for as it was said before, they had neither eaten nor drunk in all those thirteen days. Then they told many things to all men in that

city of Bethlehem and of the country round about and how wonderfully the star had brought them thither from the furthermost parts of the world.

And then, as the Evangelist has said, a message came to these Kings in their sleep that they should not return to Herod, and so by another way they went home to their lands and their kingdoms.

But the star that led them before appeared no more. And on the journey home they took their harbor and their rest on the way both by night and by day. And whereas before each King traveled with his own company, not knowing of the others, now they rode all three together with great joy and solemnity.

Furthermore these three Kings with all their men and their baggage rode through all the lands, kingdoms and provinces that Holofernes of old time had ridden and passed by with all his host; and so great was their number that all the people supposed that Holofernes had come again.

And evermore as these three Kings came into towns or cities they preached and told all the people all that they had seen, heard and done in all their way. And in all places where they came all the people worshipfully received them with great cheer and humanity. And they were so meek and so gracious to all the people that their names and their tales were never after forgotten.

Also of all the necessaries that they had carried with them on their way, there lacked or perished nothing. And so they and all their company and horses and other beasts all came home safe and whole into their own lands.

But though they had ridden out of their kingdoms in thirteen days by the leading of the star, they reached not home again but in two years. And that was so that they and all other men should know what difference there is betwixt God's working and man's working.

26

Chapter 14: Herod, in his wrath, burns the land and all the ships of Tarsus

S for Herod the King, when he heard tell that these three Kings had gone home again and had not come to him as he had charged them, then of great malice and anger he pursued after them a great way. And always as he pursued, he found that all the people blessed these Kings and praised them and told of their great nobility and array. Wherefore this Herod, in his envy and anger, burnt and destroyed all the land that was under his power that these three Kings had rid= den by, and hearing that the Kings had taken to sea secretly in the ships of Tarsus in Cilicia, he was especially angered of this city and so burned all their ships and all their goods.

27

Chapter 15: The worshipful Kings all three together visit the Hill of Vaus

O when the three Kings with all their men had come with great travail to the Hill of Vaus, which has been spoken of before, they built there a fair chapel in worship of the Child that they had gone to seek. And in the city that was under the hill, they rested. And there also they made a cove= nant that they should all three every year meet at the Hill of Vaus together with their lords and princes.

And then these Kings took their leave each of the other and every King with his people rode home again to his own land with great joy. But though they departed from each other in their bodily persons, they never did so in their hearts.

28

And when they had come to their own kingdoms, they preach=
ed and told to all their people what they had seen and heard
and done on all the way. And they made in all their temples
a star after the same form and likeness as it had appeared to
them. Wherefore many pagans left their errors and their idols
and worshiped the Child. And also the chapel that was built
on the Hill of Vaus was visited by divers people from far
countries. And the three worshipful Kings dwelt in worthy
and honest conversation until the ascension of Christ and the
coming of Saint Thomas as ye shall hear afterwards.

Chapter 16: Our Lady and Saint Joseph flee with the Christ Child into Egypt

NOW when the three Kings had gone home again to their own
lands Our Lady, for dread of the Jews, fled out of that little

Here shepherds are selling the roses of Jericho to pilgrims

house in which Christ was born and went into another dark
cave under the earth. And divers men and women loved Our
Lady Saint Mary and her Child and ministered to them all
manner of necessaries that were needful.

But when Our Lady departed from the little house she forgot
and left behind her the cloths that Christ was wound in and
her smock folded all together and laid in the hay in the manger;
and there they remained whole and clean in that same place
up to the time when Saint Helena, worshipful Queen that was
mother to King Constantine, came and found them.

Now there came the time when Our Lady dared no longer abide
in that place for dread of Herod and the Jews. And as Saint
Matthew saith in his gospel: "An angel of the Lord appeared

30

to Joseph in his sleep, saying, 'Arise and take the Child and his Mother and flee into Egypt and be there until I tell thee; for it has come to pass that Herod shall seek the Child and his Mother to slay them.' Then Joseph arose and took the Child and his Mother and fled into Egypt in the night."
Now ye shall understand that Egypt is from Bethlehem twelve days' journey. And on the way grow roses which are called roses of Jericho; and there roses grow in no other place but along the way that Our Lady rode between Bethlehem and Egypt. And shepherds of that country gather these roses at the time of blooming and sell them to pilgrims.

Chapter 17: The Holy Family dwell in Egypt for seven years in a garden with seven wells

OUR Lady Saint Mary and her Child dwelt in Egypt seven years, unto the time that Herod was dead. And the place where Our Lady dwelt with her Son is now a garden in which balm grows; and this garden is fully as long and as broad as a man may throw a stone. And in this garden are seven wells of water in which Our Lady bathed her Son and washed her clothes and her Son's clothes also.

And in this same garden are many bushes of balm, which are very like rose bushes. And in these days, to every bush a Christian man from among the Sultan's prisoners is as= signed to care for the bush and keep it clean. And this is a great marvel in the tending of these bushes that no man but a Christian may care for these bushes, for it has been oft times proven that when a Jew or a Saracen kept them, anon the bushes dried up and grew no more.

Now in the month of March the Sultan always abides in this garden; and at that time the rods of the balm bushes are cut and the balm runs out of the rods into dishes of silver. The Sultan takes all this balm into his own keeping, but if any messenger is sent from any king for balm, then the Sultan gives him a little vial full. And when this balm is all gathered the Sultan goes home and then the Christian men who are the keepers of the bushes of balm take the cut rods and boil them in water in a clean vessel. And this balm is not as full of virtue as the Sultan's balm but it is good for all manner of bruises, and if a man be wounded, it will make him whole anon. This balm is sold to divers pilgrims and so it is borne forth into the world. And all the men in the East believe truly that this place has such a virtue for growing balm because Our Lady dwelt there seven years, as was aforesaid, and bathed her Son in the wells and washed his clothes and her own in the same place.

Chapter 18: This is the story of the thirty gilt pennies which Melchior offered to the Christ Child.

 OW when Our Lady went out of Bethlehem into Egypt for dread of Herod the King, she took with her the thirty gilt pennies which Melchior had offered to her Son, along with the incense and the myrrh, bound together in a cloth. But somewhere along the road between Bethlehem and Egypt, she lost them by the way.

Now of these thirty gilt pennies ye shall hear the first beginning and the last end. Thara who was the father of Abraham made them in the name of the King of Mesopotamia. Abraham took these same thirty gilt pennies and bought with them a place for his burial and for his wife and his children. Joseph was sold by his brethren into Egypt for these same gilt pen=

33

nies. And when Jacob died these thirty gilt pennies were sent to the land of Saba to buy spices and ornaments for the burial of Jacob. Then in the time of King Solomon the queen of the land of Saba offered these thirty gilt pennies and other rich jewels to the temple of God in Jerusalem. And afterwards when by the process of time Jerusalem was destroyed, these gilt pennies were brought into the land of Arabia, of which land Melchior was king at the time that Christ was born. And Melchior offered them to God because it was the finest gold in his treasury and the best in all his land.

Now as it was aforesaid, Our Lady lost the thirty pennies and the incense and the myrrh when she was fleeing from Bethlehem for fear of Herod the King.

So afterward there was a shepherd in that country who had so great a disease that no doctor could cure him. And one time as he walked in the field with his sheep, now in one place, now in another, he found the thirty gilt pennies with the incense and the myrrh bound all together in a cloth. And he kept all these things secretly to himself until a little time before the crucifixion of Our Lord. At this time the shepherd heard of a prophet so holy that he healed all men with a word. So he came to the prophet who was Christ and prayed him for grace and help. And so great was his faith that he was healed. And when he was whole, then the shepherd offered Christ these thirty pennies with the incense and myrrh as they were bound together in one cloth. And when Our Lord saw these thirty gilt pennies with the incense and myrrh, he knew them well and bade the shepherd go to the temple and offer all these things on the altar. And the shepherd did so with great devotion.

Now a priest of the temple saw that these were honorable and glorious gifts and, in thanks, he burned the incense in a censer above the altar. And a little while after, on the third day before Christ's crucifixion, the priests of the temple took out of their common treasury the thirty gilt pennies and gave them to Judas Iscariot. And so Our Lord was sold to the Jews by the false Judas for these same thirty gilt pennies. But this false Judas was sorry for his misdeed and went to the princes of the temple and cast down again to them these thirty gilt pennies. So the Jews bought with fifteen of these pennies a field for burial for the pilgrims, as the gospel telleth, and the other fifteen pennies they gave to the knights who kept watch over the tomb of Our Lord. And one part of the myrrh the Jews mixed with the vinegar which they offered to Our Lord on the cross, and the other part of the myrrh Nicodemus, prince of the Jews, added to the aloes and other spices for the burial.

Here the shepherd offers the thirty pennies to Christ

Furthermore, the reason these thirty gilt pennies were called silver in the gospel, notwithstanding the fact that they were fine gold, is because silver is the common name for all money in that country. And many more marvels are told of these thirty gilt pennies, the which would be too long to tell.

Chapter 19: The Holy Family is told by an angel to return home from Egypt

ND when Our Lady and Joseph had dwelt in Egypt for seven years, an angel warned them to come out of Egypt, as Saint Matthew tel= leth; then they were bade to go to Galilee and there they dwelt in a city that is called Naza= reth. And what Our Lord wrought on earth from this time to his passion, the Evangelists declare openly and well.

Chapter 20: Saint Thomas the Apostle goes to India to preach the word of God

HEN Our Lord ascended into heaven after the victory and the battle that he had fought against the devil for the redemption and salvation of all mankind, he sent Saint Thomas, his apostle, into India, there to preach the word of God. In this India the three worshipful Kings at that time still reigned and were lords. And though it was against Saint Thomas' will that he went to India, ye shall understand that it was done because of the great goodness of God who wished that Saint Thomas go and preach the passion and resurrection of Christ to these three worshipful Kings who had sought God Almighty in Bethlehem at his nativity.

Now as Saint Thomas preached the word of God in the temples of India and performed many miracles by the sign of the cross, he found in every temple a star which had been painted and formed in the likeness of the star that had appeared to the three worshipful Kings on the night when Christ was born. In this star was the image of a child and the sign of a cross above.

Now when Saint Thomas saw this star, he asked of the bishops of the temples what it was. And these bishops told Saint Thomas how such a star had appeared of old time on the Hill of Vaus in token of the Child that was born to be King of the Jews and how because of this star the three Kings came out of their lands, and following the star, arrived at Bethlehem in thirteen days. And all that these three Kings had done, heard and seen, these bishops of the temples told to Saint Thomas the Apostle.

And when Saint Thomas had heard all this, he thanked God with great joy.

Chapter 21: The three Kings with all their hosts go to meet Saint Thomas the Apostle

OW the three Kings had prayed God that they should not die till they had received the sacrament of baptism, without which sacrament no man may enter into the kingdom of heaven. So when these three Kings heard that a man who was a disciple of Christ had come to their lands and was preaching to the people the works of Our Lord and especially the sacrament of baptism—anon, notwithstanding that they were of great age and feeble, yet they arrayed themselves in fine garments and came all three to Saint Thomas with other lords and princes and other multitudes of people. And Saint

Thomas received these three worthy Kings with great joy and declared to them all that Christ had taught here on earth to his disciples. Also he told them of the crucifixion of Christ, his resurrection and his ascension. He declared to them also the prophecies and many other articles of the faith. And especially he preached and informed the three Kings of the sacrament of baptism.

And when the three Kings had also told Saint Thomas how they had sought God Almighty in his childhood in Bethlehem, then Saint Thomas christened these three Kings and all the people that came with them.

And anon these three worshipful Kings were filled with the Holy Ghost and began to preach to all the people the word of God.

Saint Thomas baptises the three Kings in the Christian faith

Chapter 22: The three Kings found a rich fair city at the Hill of Vaus

HEN these three Kings with all their people went with Saint Thomas the Apostle to the Hill of Vaus; and there Saint Thomas hallowed the chapel that the three Kings had built there. And Saint Thomas and these three Kings preached to the people in that chapel concerning the Christian faith and the star that had appeared to the three Kings.

And the fame of these three Kings and of Saint Thomas spread to all the lands about and so great was their renown that all manner of men and women came from divers countries to visit the chapel on the Hill of Vaus. And from the great con= course of people that came to this chapel, the three Kings or= dained a fair city and a rich one, which is called Suwella.

Chapter 23: The three Kings are consecrated as archbishops, and they ordain other bishops and priests

OD is evermore wonderful in his works, for when Saint Thomas had thus preached and converted the people to the Christian belief, then he ordained and consecrated these three Kings as archbishops. And they then ordained other bishops, priests and clerks to serve God. Also Saint Thomas taught them all the manner and form of saying mass; also he taught them the words that Christ had said at supper the night that he was betrayed, and the Paternoster and many other things. He told them also the form of baptising and especially he charged them that they should never forget that. And when Saint Thomas had informed these three Kings and all the other people of the faith, then he went forth to other

cities and towns and preached. And then he suffered martyr=
dom for the love of Christ.

And ye shall understand that in that country where Saint
Thomas was slain, both men and women have visages like
hounds.

Chapter 24: The three Kings choose Prester John to rule after them in the city of Suwella

FTER the death of Saint Thomas these three
Kings who were archbishops did hallow all
the temples in the country to the worship of
Our Lady and cast out all the idols in the tem=
ples and ordained bishops and priests and
clerks. And to these bishops, priests and clerks the three
Kings gave many possessions to maintain God's service.

Then these three Kings forsook the vanity of the world and abode in the city of Suwella, which they had founded, as it was aforesaid; and all the people about them did venerate them and love them.

And the second year before the death of these three Kings they did call together all the kings and princes and bishops of their lands, for they were now in the last age of their lives and they had no children nor heirs; neither had they ever had queens or concubines as is the common usage of all the country. And this is found in all the writings and books of the East, though a German chronicler says the contrary of Melchior, who, according to these writings, had a wife and by her a child.

And when all the people were gathered together, the three Kings, with the assent of the people, chose a man among them who should be spiritual head in Saint Thomas' place and who should be called Patriarch Thomas. And the first patriarch that was thus chosen was a man called Jacob who had come with Saint Thomas from Antioch to India.

When the Patriarch Thomas was thus chosen, then these three Kings with the common assent of all the people chose and ordained a worshipful and mighty lord who should be temporal head and governor. And they ordained that this lord should not be called King or Emperor but Prester John, in veneration of Saint John the Evangelist and also Saint John the Baptist. And so the names of these lords continue yet unto this day.

And when this was done all the people went home again with great joy and these three Kings abode still in the city of Suwella.

Chapter 25: The three Kings die and are buried together in the same tomb

OW these three Kings lived together for two more years in the city of Suwella which they had founded near the Hill of Vaus. Then a little while before the feast of the Nativity of Our Lord Jesus Christ there appeared a wonderful star above the city, by which star the three Kings understood that the time was nigh when they should pass out of this world. Wherefore they did make a fair great tomb for their burial in the same church that they had there ordained. And in that same church these three Kings on the feast of Christ= mas did celebrate solemnly divine service.

Now on the eighth day after the birth of Christ, Melchior, who was King of Arabia and Nubia, said mass solemnly in the

44

church, and at that time he was a hundred and sixteen years old. And when he had said mass he laid himself down, and without any disease, he yielded up to Our Lord God his spirit and so died. And the other two Kings came and took his body and arrayed it with bishops' ornaments and bore him to his tomb and there they laid him.

Then on the feast of the Epiphany, Balthasar, who was King of Saba, said devoutly his mass. And when mass was done, without any grievance he passed out of this world to the bliss that is everlasting. And the years of his age were a hundred and twelve. So Jaspar, the third King, and other men took up this King; and when they had arrayed him as he should be, they laid him beside Melchior, his fellow, in the same tomb.

And then the sixth day after that, Jaspar, who was King of Tharsis, when he had offered the blessed sacrament on the altar and with all devotion had said his mass, then Christ took to him his spirit to dwell with him in everlasting joy. And so before all the people he died. And the years of his age were a hundred and nine. Then the people came and took his body and arrayed it worshipfully and bore it to the same tomb where these other two Kings lay. And then this wonder Christ showed there before all the people: when the body of the third King was brought to be laid in the tomb beside the two Kings, anon each one of the two Kings moved apart from the other and gave room for Jaspar in the middle place.

And so as these three glorious Kings lived together in life, they were not parted in their death. And these three Kings in their tomb seemed to the people not as dead bodies but as men who were asleep. And they remained whole and in= corrupt many years and days afterwards.

And the star that appeared over the city before their death abode there always still, until the bodies of the three Kings were moved away.

Chapter 26: The bodies of the three Kings are separated, each being taken to his own country

 LONG time after the death of these three Kings the Christian faith stood and was in prosperity in the worshipful city of Suwella and in all the kingdoms of the East. Then the devil through his wicked angels excited among the people divers errors and opinions of heresy in the lands of the East, and also in Suwella where these three Kings rested. And the people turned again to their old law and worshiped false gods and forsook the law of God; so that these three Kings were held in no reverence and were almost forgotten. And whereas their bodies had remained incorrupt before, now they dissolved and turned into powder.

And those people dwelling at that time in Suwella who had

46

come from the lands and kingdoms of these three Kings, each group took its King out of the tomb and put him into a separate chest and bore him home to his own land and kingdom. And there each King remained for a long time afterward, each in his own country.

Chapter 27: Many years later Saint Helena finds Our Lady's tunic and other holy relics in Bethlehem

OW when the glorious Emperor Constantine by the grace of God was converted to Christ, Saint Helena the Queen, who was mother to Constantine, was dwelling among the Jews. And she was the greatest preacher of God's law in all that country. And all the holy places that Our Lord hallowed with his body she visited, such as the hill of Cal=

vary and the place where Christ was laid in his sepulcher and the place where he appeared to Mary Magdalen in the likeness of a gardener. And above all these places this worshipful Queen built a fair church. So then she came to Bethlehem.

Now from the time that Our Lady Saint Mary had fled from Bethlehem to go into Egypt until the time when Saint Helena came, no one had gone into the dark little place where Our Lord was born—neither man nor child nor beast, for the Jews held it accursed. And when Saint Helena came there she found the same manger and the same hay that Christ had lain in and the cloths that had been wound around him and Our Lady's tunic and all those things that Our Lady forgot and left behind when she went out of that place into Egypt.

And all these holy relics Saint Helena took with her except

This is the church in Bethlehem which Saint Helena built

the manger and bore them into Constantinople, which is the chief city of Greece. Also Saint Helena did make a fair strong church of mosaic work, marble and fine gold in Bethlehem above the place where Christ was born.

Chapter 28: Saint Helena sails to India to search for the bodies of the three Kings

OW when the worshipful Saint Helena had thus visited all these holy places and ordained churches and God's ministers to serve in all these places, then she began to think greatly of the bodies of the three Kings who had worshiped God in Bethlehem at his birth. Wherefore, with certain chosen ones of her people she went forth into the lands of India.

Chapter 29: Saint Helena secures the bodies of the three Kings and returns with them to Constantinople

OW when this holy Queen Helena had come to the lands of India, anon she preached God's word to the people and destroyed all the here= sies and brought the people again to the Chris= tian faith.

And so through her preaching this Queen Helena had great renown among the people and a great love. And so when the lords of the country learned of Queen Helena's great desire for the three Kings, they gave to her the bodies of two Kings, Melchior and Balthasar. But the body of the third King, Jas= par, had been borne away by the heretics to a far distant isle. And because Helena would not that these three Kings should be parted, she made offers to the chief lords of the isle; and

in return for great gifts and also the body of Saint Thomas
the Apostle, which she had at that time in her keeping, she
received from them the body of Jaspar.

And when Saint Helena had this body of Jaspar, then she put
these three Kings together in one chest and arrayed it with
great riches and brought them to Constantinople with all joy
and reverence and put them in a fair church which is called
Santa Sophia.

Then all the people of the country about came and visited them
and made offerings with great devotion. And the bodies of
the three Kings were kept in Constantinople a long time and
God Almighty wrought there many miracles through the
merits of these three Kings.

Saint Helena with the three Kings outside Constantinople

Chapter 30: After the death of Saint Helena, the Emperor of Greece gives the bodies of the three Kings to Eustorgius of Milan

FTER the death of King Constantine and his mother Saint Helena, in the time of Julian the Apostate, there began again a new heresy and also persecution of death by sword against those that would maintain the Christian faith and the law of Christ. And after this persecution and tribu= lation the Greeks, though they had many worthy doctors and bishops, yet they forsook the law of the Holy Roman Church and chose them a Patriarch whom they yet obey to this day as we do the Pope.

And in the time of heresy the bodies and relics of the three holy Kings were held in no reverence but were utterly set at nought. And the Saracens and Turks at this time won with strong battle the lands of Greece and Armenia and destroyed a great part of these lands. But there came an Emperor of Rome, and with the help of the people of Milan, he recovered all these lands again for the Emperor of Greece.

And it is written in many books that this Emperor of Greece sent a religious man, who was named Eustorgius, into Milan on a certain mission. Now this Eustorgius was a wise man and he became powerful with the Emperor of Rome and was elected Archbishop of Milan. And when he became Archbishop he asked the Emperor of Greece to grant to him the bodies of the three worshipful Kings for the city of Milan. And the Emperor granted him his wish because he loved well this man.

So the bodies of the three Kings came to Milan and this man Eustorgius laid them in a fair church of friar-preachers with great solemnity.

Chapter 31: The bodies of the three Kings are taken to Cologne where they remain to this day

HEN afterward, by process of time, it happened that the city of Milan began to rebel against the Emperor, who was named Frederick; and this Emperor sent to the Archbishop of Cologne, who was called Rainald, for help against the city. And this Archbishop Rainald took the city of Milan and destroyed a large part thereof. During this time the great men of the city took the bodies of the three Kings and hid them secretly in the earth.

Now one of these great lords was named Asso, and the Emperor hated Asso more than all the people in the city. In the destruction of the city the Archbishop won this lord's palace

Here Archbishop Rainald brings the three Kings to Cologne

through a strong hand, and Asso was taken and put in prison. Then Asso sent word by his keepers to the Archbishop of Cologne and prayed that he might go to his presence privately and speak with him. And when Asso had come to the Archbishop he promised that if he would get him pardon of the Emperor, he would show him where the bodies of the three Kings were hidden in the earth. And when the Archbishop heard this, anon he went to the Emperor and prayed for Asso and got him pardon and good lordship.

And when this was done, then this lord Asso brought secretly the bodies of these three Kings to the Archbishop of Cologne; and in great secret the Archbishop sent these bodies by his own private company a long way outside the city of

54

Milan. And then the Archbishop went to the Emperor and asked that he grant him the bodies of these three Kings. And the Emperor granted them to him with good will. And ye shall understand that the Archbishop would not speak to the Emperor before about the bodies of the three Kings because he was in doubt whether the Emperor would grant them to him or not.

And so the Archbishop openly and with great procession brought these holy saints, the three Kings, into Cologne and there he put them in the fair church of Saint Peter worship=fully. And all the people of the country with great reverence received these holy relics. And they are kept and are venerated by all manner of nations until this day.

And thus endeth the story of these three worshipful Kings, Melchior, Balthasar and Jaspar.

Chapter 32: All peoples from the lands of the East show de=votion to the three Kings

OW ye shall understand that in all the lands and kingdoms where these three Kings were lords and in all the lands of the East all manner of people, though they be heretics and schis=matics, have devotion to these three Kings and the feast of the Epiphany, as ye shall now hear.

Of the sects of heretics, those of the kingdom of Arabia and Nubia, where Melchior was king, are true Christian men. And the priests of this country when they go to the altar have on their heads crowns of gold, or else silver=gilt, in memory of the three Kings.

And the heretics of the land of Saba where Balthasar was king, though partly corrupt in the faith, have reverence for the three Kings. Their priests when they sing mass bear gold

Here the clergy of Balthasar's land bear gold, incense and myrrh to the altar

in their hands to the altar and the deacons bear incense and the subdeacons, myrrh.

But the other sect, which is of the kingdom of Tharsis where Jaspar was king, are the worst heretics of all. And their priests when they go to mass curse all men who were of help in taking away the body of their king, Jaspar. Now these here=tics are for the most part black Ethiopes, and they paint God and Our Lady and the three Kings in their churches all black and the devil all white. And this they do despite all other Christian men.

Also there is another sect in the land of India which is Prester John's land. And these are good Christian men. The priests of this land when they say mass hang a crown of gold above

56

the altar. And the priest and the deacon and the subdeacon meet from different parts of the church, and then go to the altar. This they do in token that the three Kings met together from three different ways on a highway outside Jerusalem and then by the leading of the star rode into Bethlehem and offered gifts to God Almighty.

And of another sect, which is in Syria, there is but little heresy. And these men when they swear before the justice for any cause, they swear by the gospel and the three Kings.

And also the sect of the Greeks when they say mass cut the bread in a square and this bread they put in a dish of gold or of silver, and above that they lay a star and cover it with

Here the bishop of Jaspar's land curses the people who were of help in taking away the body of Jaspar

a fair white cloth. And after the offertory of the mass they take this dish with the host and with the star and they carry it about the church on their heads with censers and candles and great reverence. And this they do in token that these three Kings with great gifts sought God Almighty in Bethlehem and through the leading of the star came to the manger where he lay and there fell down and worshiped him.

Here the priest of the Greek Church carries a square host on his head

Furthermore, all sects of Christian men in the East, though they be heretics, fast on Christmas Eve until the night and then every man sets forth on his board enough meat and drink to suffice him from Christmas Day to Epiphany. And of this meat and drink they feast with their wives and their children

58

Here the Christian men worship on Twelfth Night at the river Jordan

with all mirth and joy in this time. Also they light a candle or lamp that shall burn night and day from Christmas to Twelfth Night beside the same board. And on the vigil of the Epiphany at night each man goes to his friend's house with a candle in his hand and when he cometh he says "Good day," for if he were to say "Good evening," it would be considered great trespass. And so they go from house to house all night long and eat and drink and dance and bear lighted candles in their hands in token of the star that appeared to lead these three Kings and all their hosts to Bethlehem—when there was no night but was evermore day to them.

Also on Twelfth Night all manner of Christian men come from far countries to the river Jordan with their bishops and priests, with crosses of silver and censers. And when all the people have come to the river, which is from Jerusalem but five miles, then every sect stands together in a certain place. And every sect reads in his own tongue the gospel story of the three Kings. And when the gospel is read, then every sect with great devotion worships his cross, and makes offerings every man in his power, and this is done in memory of the offerings of the three Kings to God Almighty.

Also the Saracens, that are of Mohammet's law, and other Turks have these three Kings in special reverence. For in all the temples in their country that were at one time Christian they have defaced the images; with their knives they have cut off the noses of the images and put out their eyes for spite.

These are Saracens defacing the holy statues

But the images of these three Kings they suffer to stand without any harming.

And many divers sects of Christian men have many other special devotions to these three worshipful Kings—the which were too long to tell. But ye shall understand that in all countries in the East, all manner of people have these three Kings in great reverence and devotion. And Our Lord Jesus Christ showed many miracles in divers countries of the East through the merits and prayers of these three worthy Kings, who are now in the high bliss of heaven.

To this bliss may He bring us, He who in heaven sitteth above all kings and reigneth without end. Amen.

Concerning
John of Hildesheim
and his book

A view of the city of Cologne. The cathedral which houses the shrine of the three Kings is shown under construction in the illustration. The nave was not completed until the nineteenth century.
Woodcut from the *Cologne Chronicle* (Cologne, 1499). The Pierpont Morgan Library

AT THE TIME that John of Hildesheim (Johannes Hildeshemensis) wrote his *Story of the Three Kings* the Magi were among the best-loved saints of Christendom. As John says in his Prologue: "Of the three worshipful Kings all the world is full of praise from the rising of the sun to its downgoing." Legends and tales about them had been accumulating for over twelve hundred years, but no one had put the whole story of the three Kings together in one book. And so at the request of Florenz of Wevelkoven, Bishop of Münster, John of Hildesheim undertook the job. Since Florenz became bishop in 1364 and John died in 1375, the *Story of the Three Kings* must have been written sometime between these two dates.

John of Hildesheim was a friar of the Carmelite order with a learned, cosmopolitan background that undoubtedly contributed much to the richness of his book. As a young man he was sent by his order to study for his doctorate in Avignon at a time when the papal court was in that city and emissaries from countries all over the world were gathered there. In 1358 he was appointed instructor in the Sacred Scriptures at the University of Paris, one of the great theological centers of the Middle Ages. Later, in Germany, as prior of the Convent of the Carmelites at Cassel, he went to chapter meetings in Cologne and other cities of the Empire, and in 1366 was sent on a mission to Rome.

In all these places, he apparently kept his eyes and his ears open, for he says in the Prologue to his book that some of his information about the three Kings was from "hearing and speaking to other men." He undoubtedly spoke to many a pilgrim returned from the Holy Land. such as Ludolph of Suchem, whose tales of the roses of Jericho and the garden of balm in Egypt (*De itinere terrae sanctae*, or *Journey to the Holy Land*, written 1350-1361) are followed very closely by John. He may have talked to world travelers (and there were many besides Marco Polo in the thirteenth and fourteenth centuries) and learned about the "black Ethiopes" who painted their holy statues "all black and the devils all white." (Marco Polo reported a people like this in the region where Saint Thomas died.) John undoubtedly listened to tales of the mysterious Prester John, who was supposed to be of the race of the three Magi and ruler of a rich and powerful Christian kingdom in "India." (There was much talk and conjecture about this fabulous character in John's day.) At that time, before printing was invented, one had to depend a great deal for information on "hearing and speaking to other men." And if John did not always question the credibility of these tales of the fabulous East, one must not blame him too much, for in the Middle Ages almost anything that was reported about the East was believed. And if what was reported did not seem unbelievable, it was considered disappointing.

John's *Story of the Three Kings*, as he himself says, was also based on "seeing." His description of the Virgin Mary as "somewhat brown, [with] her head covered altogether save her face with a linen cloth," and of the Child as "somewhat fat" may be the result of John's "seeing" so many Italian Madonnas painted by Sienese artists in Avignon when he was a student there. His setting of the Nativity as "a little unthrifty house before the cave" may also derive from seeing the same setting in many a fourteenth-century Italian painting of the Nativity.

It is also highly probable that John saw liturgical plays of the three Kings at Christmas time in France, where they were very popular, or in Germany. In these plays the clergy who acted the parts of the three Kings were directed to "come each from his own corner, as if from his own region," and "meet together before the altar." John's description of the meeting of Melchior, Balthasar and Jaspar at the junction of the three highways outside Jerusalem follows the Church plays and is contrary to other versions of the legend in which the three Kings see the star together and make the whole journey in each other's company. In the liturgical plays the three Kings often meet the shepherds returning from the manger. John may have borrowed his incident also from seeing such a play.

John's vivid description of the "multitude" of people who accompanied the three Kings on their journey, along with "the mules and camels and horses loaded with treasure," may have been due to his having witnessed one of the sumptuous and elaborately staged processions of the Magi, presented in Milan each year, beginning in 1336, at the Feast of the Epiphany. In these performances the cavalcade of the Kings, made up of crowds of richly arrayed people and beasts laden with boxes and bales of treasure, paraded through the streets of Milan to the Church of Saint Eustorgius where the "Magi" presented their gifts at the Altar of the Three Kings.

Besides "seeing and hearing and speaking to other men," John says that he used sermons and homilies for his *Story of the Three Kings*. As a former instructor in the Sacred Scriptures, he was familiar not only with the Old and the New Testaments (which he quotes scrupulously) but also with commentators on the Scriptures who, from the second century on, sought to explain and elucidate the story of the "wise men from the East" as told by the good Saint Matthew in "his gospel that he wrote." Saint Matthew never said that the wise men were kings, but in the second century Tertullian associated them with the kings of the Psalms: "The kings of Tharsis and the isles shall offer gifts, the kings of the Arabians and of Saba shall bring presents. And all the kings of the earth shall adore him." These verses were introduced as an important part of the liturgy for Epiphany and soon the Magi of Matthew, from being likened to kings, indeed became kings in the minds of the people.

John of Hildesheim does not question their royalty. In fact, he explains that the reason the three Kings were called Magi originally was because of ignorance on the part of the pagans and envy on the part of the Jews. Ludolph of Saxony, a contemporary of John's, in his popular *Vita Christi (Life of Christ)* argues more reasonably: "The three pagan Kings were called Magi not because they were magicians but because of the great science of astrology which was theirs. Those whom the Hebrews called scribes and the Greeks, philosophers, and the Latins, wise men, the Persians called Magi. And the reason that they were called Kings is that in those days it was the custom for the philosophers and wise men to be rulers...Oh what a difference there is in the government at the present time."

Since the Gospel of Saint Matthew does not mention the number of "wise men," commentators on the Scriptures discussed this problem also. It was Origen (about 185 A.D.—about 254 A.D.) who first suggested that the number was three, presumably basing his conclusion on the three gifts: gold, frankincense and myrrh. Many East-Christian writers, however, maintained that there were twelve. This latter point of view is reflected in John's account of the twelve astronomers who watched on the Hill of Vaus. As for the Kings themselves, John never seems to

doubt for a moment that they were three.

His conception of the third King as a "black Ethiope" had its origin in sermons and homilies which also related the Magi to the Psalms: "Princes shall come out of Egypt; Ethiopia shall soon stretch out her hands to God," and, "The Ethiopians shall bow down before him..." Saint Jerome (about 340-420 A.D.) furthered the idea of a "black Ethiope" by suggesting that the Magi represented the three sons of Noah, and thereby, the three races of man. In the twelfth century a German commentator first stated definitely that the third King was black, and John says for emphasis that he was a "black Ethiope without any doubt."

Theologians gave considerable thought also to the meaning of the gifts: gold, frankincense and myrrh. John accepts the reasoning of the majority that gold was offered to Christ as King, incense to him as God, and myrrh as to a man who would suffer and die. He rejects the more practical interpretation of Saint Bernard in the twelfth century that gold was given to Mary "to relieve her poverty, incense against the stench of the stable...and myrrh...to put away vermin."

From sermons and homilies John derived several of the episodes in his story. In the sixth century Arnobius the Younger had connected the ships of Tarsus in the Psalms (48) with Herod and the Magi. By the twelfth century it was generally accepted as a fact that the Magi escaped from Herod by embarking for home in ships of Tarsus and that Herod in his anger burned all the vessels in the harbor.

John's account of the "cloud and...the darkness" which settled on the Magi outside Jerusalem was developed from early sermons associating the Magi with the prophecy of Isaiah: "Arise, be enlightened, O Jerusalem, for thy light is come, and the glory of the Lord is risen upon thee. For behold, the darkness shall cover the earth and a mist the people; but the Lord shall arise upon thee, and his glory shall be seen upon thee. And the Gentiles shall walk in the light, and the kings in the brightness of thy rising... The multitude of camels shall cover thee, the dromedaries of Madian and Epha; all they from Saba shall come, bringing gold and frankincense, and showing forth praise to the Lord." John has taken the prophecy literally and has expanded it into an incident of considerable dramatic power.

Of the "divers" books that John used for his *Story of the Three Kings,* he makes special note of "certain books written in Hebrew and Chaldean" (later translated into French), which had been brought out of "India" by the princes of Vaus when they came to Acre in the year 1200. It has so far been impossible to identify these princes of Vaus or their mysterious books. It is highly probable, however, that John's account of the thirty golden pennies came from such a source. It is known that this elaborate tale of the pieces of gold which Melchior offered to Christ originated in the East (and was not invented by John, as Carl Horstmann suggested in 1886). It was used by Godfrey of Viterbo before 1191 and by Ludolph of Suchem between 1350 and 1361.

It was an Eastern writer of the early centuries who invented names for the Magi. They first appear in Latin form in the West about the seventh century. These names, Melchior, Balthasar and Jaspar, are found with various spellings at different times and in different places. And since nobody in authority knew exactly which name belonged to which king, the combination varied according to the commentator. A large proportion of contemporary German writers, however, named the three Kings as John does.

John's chapter on the twelve astrologers and his account of the baptism of the three Kings were derived from a work attributed in John's day to Saint John Chrysostom but now known to have been written not earlier than the sixth century by an unknown writer in the East. The author of this so-called *Apocryphal Book of Seth* says of his work: *Etsi non certa, non tamen destruente fidem, sed potius delectante.* (Though this is not certain, it nevertheless does not destroy belief, but rather, gives delight.)

John of Hildesheim used his sources with about as much critical inquiry as the author of the *Book of Seth.* Though John was a Doctor of Divinity, a teacher of the Sacred Scriptures, and a respected prior of the order of the Carmelites, he accepted and included in his book much that was "not certain," but nevertheless gave delight. His account of the translation of the bodies of the three Kings from Milan to Cologne, however, has some foundation in history. According to the chronicles, in the year 1158 the people of Milan rebelled against their Emperor, Frederick Barbarossa, and were subdued. In the same year the bodies of the three Magi were "discovered in an old Church [Church of Saint Eustorgius] near the city of Milan and for fear of Frederick were removed and placed inside the city." In 1159 Milan again rebelled, and when it finally surrendered in 1162, it was pillaged and then destroyed by fire. Among the spoils which Barbarossa distributed as rewards to those who had supported him in his Italian con-

The abbess presenting the relics of the three Kings to Rainald of Dassel, Archbishop of Cologne. The reliquary in the illustration bears no resemblance to the shrine made (about 1180-about 1215) for the relics of the Kings and still to be seen in the Cathedral of Cologne.
Woodcut from *Chronik der Sachsen* (Mainz, 1492). The Pierpont Morgan Library

flicts were the bodies of the three Kings. These he gave in 1164 to Rainald of Dassel, Imperial Chancellor and Archbishop of Cologne, who was fully aware of the value of this princely gift. On the eleventh day of June in the year 1164 Rainald set out with the precious relics from Pavia in Italy; he traveled by way of Vercelli, Turin, Vienne (France), through Lotharingia and down the Rhine to Cologne where he arrived safely on the twenty-third day of July. A letter still exists which Rainald sent ahead by special messenger to announce the coming of the bodies of the three Kings and to request a worthy reception for them. Apparently there was some doubt about the authenticity of these relics at the time, however, for one chronicler wrote: "On the eleventh day of this month [June, 1164], Rainald, Chancellor and Archbishop of

Cologne, took the bodies of the martyred saints Nabor and Felix…and *three other bodies* that were buried in the tomb in the church of the blessed Eustorgius that were *said* to be the three Magi, and carried them away with him to Cologne." (Italics are mine.)

Marco Polo could not have believed in the authenticity of the Cologne relics, for he says in his *Description of the World* (1299) that he saw the bodies of the three Kings in Persia: "In Persia is the city called Saba from which the three Magi set out when they came to worship Jesus Christ; and in this city they are buried in three very large and very beautiful sepulchres side by side…The bodies are still all whole, with hair and beards remaining." Other travelers also reported seeing the tombs of the three Kings in the East. John, however, never doubts that the "three other bodies" which Rainald of Dassel brought back from Milan to Cologne were the bodies of the "three worshipful Kings." And it must be said that there are many indications that most of the Western world concurred with John in this belief. Pilgrims flocked from all countries to Cologne to see the beautiful jeweled and gilded shrine containing the relics of the three Kings, a pope in 1327 issued a bull to further the building of the new cathedral in Cologne worthy to house the relics of the "sainted Kings," and the fair city of Cologne displayed the three crowns of the Kings on its coat of arms. Indeed, they were quite generally known as the Three Kings of Cologne.

John's account of how Saint Helena found the bodies of the three Kings and brought them to Constantinople and how Eustorgius transported the three Kings from Constantinople to Milan are based

68

on sources which are not earlier than the late twelfth century. These sources, the *Life of Saint Eustorgius* and others, were written *after* the "discovery" of the three Kings in Milan and were undoubtedly intended to explain that "discovery." What could be more probable than that Saint Helena had found the three Kings in India, since she had found the True Cross? What could be more logical than that Bishop Eustorgius should have brought the three Kings from Constantinople, since the bodies of the three Kings were discovered in his church in Milan? Such

A city gate of Cologne showing the coats of arms of the three Kings and *(below, right)* the arms of the city of Cologne with the crowns of the three Kings, often called the Three Kings of Cologne.
Woodcut from *Chronik der Sachsen* (Mainz, 1492). The Pierpont Morgan Library

69

explanations filled in the story neatly, they were not too incredible, and they were pleasant additions to the tale.

John's tale of the Milanese nobleman who exchanged the bodies of the three Kings in return for his freedom is also apocryphal. The story first appeared in the thirteenth century; then, in John's day, the name of the nobleman was added. Asso (Azzo della Torre) belonged to one of the most powerful families in Milan. Slightly different versions of the incident appear in the later *Cologne Chronicle* and the *Saxon Chronicle*. In these chronicles, it is an abbess who had the bodies of the three Kings in her keeping, and since her brother, who held office as mayor of Milan, was about to be hanged for his insurrection, she bought his life with the relics of the three Kings.

Perhaps enough has now been said to give an idea of the kind of material that John of Hildesheim gathered together for his *Story of the Three Kings*. Whether he contributed any completely new incidents to the legend of the Magi, it is impossible to determine unless one can discover those mysterious books which the "princes of Vaus" brought out of "India." One is inclined to think, however, that John preferred to have some kind of testimony for all the major events he related, and that his sense of integrity would never have allowed him to invent out of whole cloth, as Carl Horstmann has suggested, such a sequence as that of the thirty gold pennies. But John was a good storyteller

and one would guess that he added a bit here and expanded a bit there in order to make a scene more dramatic or an incident more appealingly human. For instance, he tells us what Mary wore when the three Kings came; why the three Kings offered only gold, frankincense and myrrh though they had brought with them great treasures; how the three Kings were able to understand each other though they spoke different languages; and how they disported themselves at the inn after they had worshiped the Child.

Other people had written about the interest of the Chaldeans in the study of the stars but John adds the comment that "every maid and every child in men's houses did know the course of the stars." French poems and liturgical plays told how the three Kings met and talked to the shepherds, but John says that the three Kings also gave to the shepherds "great gifts." Others had spoken briefly of the return journey of the Magi but John says further: "Whereas before each King traveled with his own company, not knowing of the others, now they rode all three together with great joy and solemnity"; and "when these Kings took their leave each of the other...though they departed from each other in their bodily persons, they never did so in their hearts."

One feels that John "put together" into one book not only a collection of other men's tales and other men's thoughts but also added to the story of the three Kings some enjoyable imaginings of his own.

Adoration of the Magi,
with a ruined castle
as the setting.
Woodcut from *Auslegung des
Lebens Jesu Christi* (Ulm, about
1478). The Metropolitan
Museum of Art

Concerning
John of Hildesheim's influence
on Nativity scenes in art

MEDIEVAL ART, which so often told a story or preached a sermon or explained a concept, was to a large extent influenced by the written and spoken word and dependent on it. And conversely, the word was sometimes influenced by the art. It has already been suggested in the foregoing text that John of Hildesheim quite possibly derived his descriptions of the Virgin and Child from looking at Italian paintings. It is probable that John's story in turn had in at least one respect a far-reaching effect on artists who came after him. He seems to have introduced ruins into the Nativity scenes.

In John's day and before, artists of Byzantium and most of the artists of Italy had regularly depicted the Nativity as taking place in a cave or grotto in accordance with the story as told in the Protevangelion and other apocryphal gospels. Sometimes, especially in fourteenth-century Italy, a little shelter was added in front of the cave. The artists of France, Germany, Flanders and England, however, usually omitted the grotto, showing the stable as a small structure aboveground. Then along came John who conceived of the place of the Nativity as a combination of a little hut, cave, and the house of David, which of course was so old that it had fallen into ruins by the time Christ was born. "Bethlehem was but a castle," John wrote, "but it was called a city because King David was born there ...and in the same place Christ, God's Son, was born...But at the time of the nativity of Our Lord, that house was all destroyed insomuch that there was nothing left but broken walls on every side and a little cave under the earth and a little unthrifty house before the cave."

John's description of David's castle with "broken walls on every side" as a setting for the Nativity seems to have fascinated late medieval painters, carvers and printmakers, especially those of Germany and Flanders. Ruins were picturesque, ruins were a challenge to the artist of skill, and ruins became almost as important to the Nativity scene as Joseph or the angels, or the ox and the ass. That the vogue for ruins came almost a century after John of Hildesheim first wrote his description of them is typical of the time lag in the Middle Ages between the new in literary expression and the corresponding image in art.

Albrecht Dürer's Adoration of the Magi shows a setting of broken walls on every side, as described by John of Hildesheim.
Woodcut, made about 1505, from the Life of the Virgin (Nuremberg, 1511). The Metropolitan Museum of Art

73

Bibliography

This brief bibliography includes the medieval books mentioned in the Notes and a few other publications that were of special value in preparing this study. There are many other books and articles which also helped but to list them all would be wearisome to everybody and, as John would say, "too long to tell."

MEDIEVAL

Botho, Conrad. *Chronik der Sachsen.* Mainz (Peter Schoeffer), 1492

This chronicle provided two woodcut illustrations for the Notes and an interesting medieval account of the acquisition by Rainald of Dassel of the relics of the three Kings.

Cologne Chronicle. Cologne (Johann Koelhoff), 1499

One of the illustrations for the Notes was taken from this chronicle, as well as information concerning the rebellion of Milan and the transfer of the relics of the three Kings.

John of Hildesheim. *The Three Kings of Cologne.* Edited by Carl Horstmann. Published for the Early English Text Society, Original Series, Vol. LXXXIII, London, 1886

This volume contains the two English manuscripts and a Latin version of John of Hildesheim's *Story of the Three Kings* which were the basis for the present story. Horstmann's introduction was extremely useful for the notes on the life of John of Hildesheim and for details concerning the translation of the relics of the three Kings from Milan to Cologne.

Ludolph of Saxony. *Vita Christi.* Paris (for Ambroise Girault), about 1530

This *Life of Christ*, written in the fourteenth century, provided the interesting medieval explanation for calling the three Kings "Magi."

Ludolph of Suchem. *Journey to the Holy Land.* Translated from the Latin and edited by Aubrey Stewart. *Palestine Pilgrims' Text Society*, no. 27, London, 1895

Ludolph's account of a journey to the Holy Land was written about 1350-1361. He tells of the roses of Jericho, the thirty gilt pennies, pilgrims gathering at the river Jordan on Twelfth Night and the balm garden in Egypt, more or less as John does.

Polo, Marco. *The Description of the World.* 2 vols. Translated and edited by A. C. Maule and Paul Pelliot. London, 1938

Marco Polo wrote about seeing the tomb of the Magi in Persia.

MODERN

Clemen, Paul. *Der Dom zu Köln.* Die Kunstdenkmäler der Rheinprovinz, Vol. VI, Part 3. Düsseldorf, 1937

An excellent discussion of the history of the Cathedral of Cologne and its treasures

Hill, G. F. "The Thirty Pieces of Silver." *Archaeologia,* Vol. LIX, Part 2. London, 1905

The story of the thirty gilt pennies

Kehrer, Hugo. *Die Heiligen Drei Könige in Literatur und Kunst.* 2 vols. Leipzig, 1909

This comprehensive publication was valuable in tracing the various steps in the development of the legend of the Magi.

Mâle, Emile. *L'Art religieux du XIIe siècle en France.* Paris, 1924
—*L'Art religieux du XIIIe siècle en France.* Paris, 1925

—*L'Art religieux de la fin du moyen age en France.* Paris, 1925

These three volumes by Emile Mâle provided the starting point for my study of the iconography of the Magi many years ago.

Schnitzler, Hermann. *Der Dreikönigenschrein.* Bonn, 1939

One of the many books giving the history of the shrine of the three Kings in Cologne

Sturdevant, Winifred. "The Misterio de los Reyes Magos." *Johns Hopkins Studies in Romance Literatures and Languages,* Vol. X, Baltimore, 1927

This paper was of help in tracing the development of the legend of the Magi.

Young, Karl. *The Drama of the Medieval Church.* Oxford, 1933

A comprehensive study of liturgical plays, including those of the three Kings

Contents

76

Illustrations

Many people have been of great help in getting this little book ready for publication and I wish to thank them all, especially Bonnie Young, Olga Krupen and Marshall B. Davidson of the Museum staff, Curt Bühler and Mark Brewer of The Pierpont Morgan Library and Franz C. Hess of Huxley House.

M. B. F., 1955

The illustrations for *The Story of the Three Kings,* as noted in the Foreword, are from a copy of the Strassburg (Knoblochtzer) edition, generally dated 1484, in The Pierpont Morgan Library. The reproductions are actual size and preserve all the irregularities and inequalities of the originals in that copy. As in the old edition certain woodcuts have been repeated. The ornamental initials are retouched letters from other fifteenth-century books printed in Germany.

The book is set in Wallau, a type face designed between 1925 and 1930 by the noted German calligrapher and designer Rudolf Koch, who patterned it after a fourteenth-century manuscript in the rotunda style. Named after Heinrich Wallau, scholar and printer of Mayence who in 1885 had pointed to the possibility of developing a useful modern face from the Italian rotunda, the Wallau retains Gothic characteristics and suggests the type of the Strassburg book from which illustrations are taken. The type was specially imported for the first printing of this book.

This impression was printed by Eilert Printing Company, New York, New York, and bound by Publishers Book Bindery, Long Island City, New York. The book was designed by Franz C. Hess of Huxley House. The cover, jacket and title page were designed by Katy Homans.

80